EGMONT
We bring stories to life

First published in Great Britain in 2011
by Egmont UK Limited,
239 Kensington High Street,
London W8 6SA

Editor: Catherine Such • Art Editor: Amanda Hartley
Designer: Stacy Cleater • Writer: Deborah Nash
Editorial Assistant: Hannah Greenfield
Group Art Editor: Jeanette Ryall • Group Editor: Keilly Swift

ISBN 978 1 4052 5643 8
1 3 5 7 9 10 8 6 4 2
Printed in China

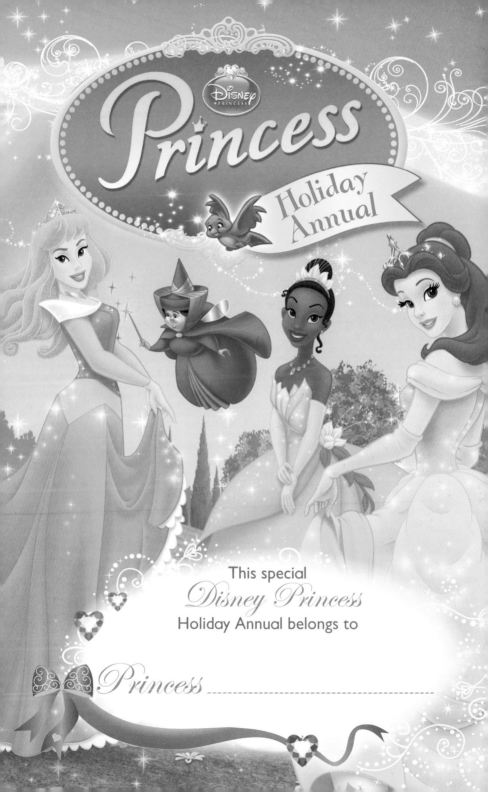

Princess

Holiday Annual

This special
Disney Princess
Holiday Annual belongs to

Princess ....

Disney Princess

Holiday Annual

Sticker Play
Use your pretty princess stickers inside.

All this inside …

All About
Princess Ariel

A Mermaid's World

Ariel, the little princess
who lives in a sea palace,
has six older sisters and lots
of fish friends. She is curious
about everything, including
the human world. Find out
more here …

Ariel has found some lovely pearls in a shell! Add a splash of colour!

Sticker Play

Add some jewellery stickers to Ariel.

I can count ♥ starfish.

Answer on page 90.

King Triton

King Triton is Ariel's
father. He worries about
his youngest daughter
and is not pleased when
Ariel falls in love
with a human.

Sebastian

A red crab servant,
Sebastian is court composer.
He clicks his pincers, dances
and sings. King Triton asks
him to watch over Ariel and
keep her out of trouble.

Flounder

Flounder is a yellow and
blue tropical fish and Ariel's
best friend. He is sensitive
and panics when he finds
himself in frightening
situations.

Prince Eric

Prince Eric is a human
prince who dives into
the sea to rescue his dog.
Ariel spots the prince in the
water and falls head
over tail in love.

Precious Treasure

Ariel loves to explore
shipwrecks looking for
treasure. Draw your
most precious treasure
in this space.

How many
seahorses can
you count on
these two
pages?

Answer on page 90.

Ariel's Secret Diary

I'm always getting into trouble, usually with my daddy, King Triton. Take a peek inside my secret diary to find out what happened when I was sent to finishing school …

Dear Diary ...

Today started off really well. I swam down
to the seabed and made friends with a twirly sea
anemone. I was so busy playing, I forgot all about
the birthday party at the palace for granny.
I arrived just as it was finishing.

Daddy wasn't very happy at all ...

Dear Diary ...

Oh dear, Daddy is still upset with me. He told me today that he's sending me to finishing school! Can you believe it? All my sisters went so he thinks it will do me good.

I'm not looking forward to it at all ...

Dear Diary ...

I'm in trouble already and I've only been to one class! We had to swim with shells on our heads to help us move gracefully.

It was a bit boring, so I decided to throw my shell like a frisbee instead! Soon, everyone had joined in.

The headmistress didn't find it very funny ...

Dear Diary ...

Uh-oh, I'm in trouble again! This time it was in synchronised swimming class. We were floating about to classical music when I decided to liven things up a bit. Soon, we were rocking and rolling and wiggling and jiggling. It was so much fun.

But the headmistress didn't agree!

Well, it had to happen didn't it? I got called to the headmistress's office. "You have behaved like a silly seahorse," she said to me. "What would your father say if he heard about this?"

I know what Daddy would say. He'd tug his beard and sigh, "Why can't you behave like a princess!"

I'm in trouble, from head to tail.

Dear Diary ...

You are not going to believe this. I can't believe it!
Guess who was the star pupil in class today? Who
was quiet and on time? Who made the best ball
gown? Who was really, really good? Me!

For the first time ever, I saw the headmistress smile ...

Dear Diary ...

After weeks of being good, it's time for me to leave finishing school.

Today was graduation day so I got to dress up in a pretty gown. When I received my certificate, everyone flapped their fins and Flounder blew bubbles. Daddy was so proud of me.

I think I'll carry on being good ... at least until tomorrow!

The end

Sticker Play

Add a sticker when you have finished reading the story.

Put your sticker here.

Mer-mysteries

Join Ariel and her friends under the sea
to solve these fun puzzles.

1

a What colour is King Triton's tail?

b What is King Triton holding in his hand?

c Can you see King Triton's gold trident?

2 What would Ariel most like to find on the seabed? Use the key to crack the code.

Key

p	i	r	s
a	n	l	e

Colour Ariel's turtle friend.

Sea Shadows

Draw lines to match the shadows below to Ariel's friends.

1

Colour the fish to complete the scene.

a

2

b

3

c

5

f

4

6

e

d

Sticker Play
Add a sticker when you have finished the activity.

Put your sticker here.

Which shell comes next in this sequence below?

Answers on page 90.

23

Princess Fun

Can you help the princesses complete these magical activities?

Dream Time

1 Here are frogs Tiana and Prince Naveen in the bayou. Give them some night-time colours.

Which Dwarf?

2 Read the clues in order to work out which Dwarf Snow White is thinking of.

a

b

c

d

e

f

g

He has a white beard.

He has a yellow hat.

He is wearing glasses.

Snow White is thinking of

Answer on page 90.

25

Magic Lamps

Put the magic lamps in order of size, starting with the smallest. Write your answers in the hearts.

3

Smallest

Largest

Answers on page 90.

Pretty Pieces

4

Can you work out which princess is in each close-up?

b

c

a

Add some magical colours to finish this pretty picture of Snow White and Tiana.

27

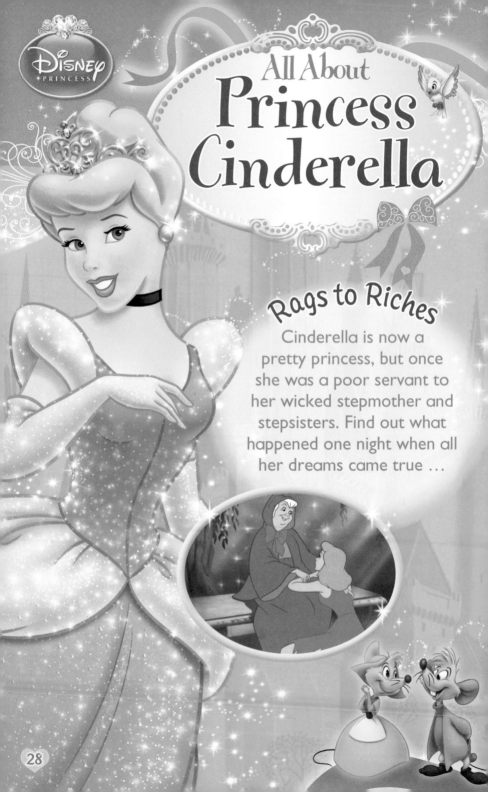

All About
Princess Cinderella

Rags to Riches

Cinderella is now a pretty princess, but once she was a poor servant to her wicked stepmother and stepsisters. Find out what happened one night when all her dreams came true …

Here's Cinderella singing to some birds. Give them all some pretty colours.

Sticker Play

Choose a tiara sticker for Cinderella to wear.

I can count ♡ birds.

Answer on page 90.

Dreams Come True

Cinderella dreamed of going to the ball, but her stepmother and stepsisters made her do the chores. Then an unexpected visitor arrived to help …

Fairy Friend

Cinderella's fairy godmother waved her wand and gave Cinderella a beautiful dress and glass slippers. A horse and carriage whisked her away to the ball!

Prince Charming

Cinderella spent the night dancing with Prince Charming. At midnight, the spell ended and she had to go, leaving a glass slipper behind.

Happy Ending

Prince Charming looked for the owner of the glass slipper and found his love, Cinderella. They were married and lived happily ever after.

Your Wish

If you had a fairy godmother to grant you one wish, what would it be? Write it here.

....

....

....

....

Cinderella's Secret Diary

I have lots of secrets to share with you. Take a look inside my secret diary to find out about a magical surprise I gave my fairy godmother …

Dear Diary ...

After everything my fairy godmother has done for me, I'd really like to help her in return and I think I know how.

She has an invitation to the Fairy Ball, but she doesn't have anything new to wear. Fairies can't use magic on themselves, so I have a plan ...

Dear Diary ...

Today, when my fairy godmother wasn't looking,
I borrowed her magic wand and spell book.
I waved the wand and said `Make a gorgeous
fairy gown!´ but guess what happened?

A pair of curtains appeared!
I will try again tomorrow.

Dear Diary ...

I thought I'd try to magic up
something smaller today.
I waved the wand and said
`Make a beautiful,
sparkling necklace!'
but do you know what
appeared? A very long,
silk scarf!

I don't think I'm very good
at magic, but I won't give up!

Dear Diary ...

Today, I decided to try my luck with some shoes.
I waved the wand and said `Make a pair of magical
dancing shoes´ but instead, a pair of pink, fluffy
slippers appeared!

I wonder if my animal friends can help me?

Dear Diary ...

My animal friends are amazing! I showed them the curtains, the scarf and the slippers and they had a wonderful idea. We can turn them into a beautiful outfit.

I'll just grab my sewing kit and we'll get to work!

Dear Diary ...

My friends and I have created the most
beautiful ball gown, with lovely bows and
pretty sparkles. We turned the slippers into
gorgeous dancing shoes, too! I can't wait to
show my fairy godmother!

Dear Diary ...

All our hard work was worth it! My fairy godmother was delighted with her new outfit and she even won first prize at the Fairy Ball. She was pleased to have her wand and spell book back, too.

I learned a good lesson though ... true magic doesn't come from a wand, it comes from a friend's heart.

The end

Sticker Play

Add a sticker when you have finished reading the story.

Put your sticker here.

Cinderella's New Dress

Can you find five differences in picture b?

Put your sticker here.

Put your sticker here.

Put your sticker here.

Put your sticker here.

Put your sticker here.

b

Perfect Outfit

Imagine you're going to the ball with Cinderella!
Choose the outfit you would like to wear.

Dresses

Sticker Play

Put a jewel sticker next to your favourite dress, shoes and tiara.

Shoes

Tiaras

Now all you need is some jewellery. Draw a necklace to match the outfit you have chosen.

Princess Fun

The princesses have some enchanting puzzles just for you.

Lily Pond Life

1 Can you match the shadows to the creatures in the lily pond? Which one isn't in the pond?

a

b

c

d

Baking Day **2**

sugar

apples

berries

butter

carrot

flour

Circle the item you wouldn't usually find in a fruit pie.

The pie is baked! Give Snow White some fruity colours.

Starry Night

3

Can you help Jasmine find her way through the cloud maze to Aladdin?

How many stars can you count along the way?

Start

Finish

46

Story Time

4

Put these three scenes from *The Princess and the Frog* in order of the story. Write the correct numbers in the circles.

a

b

c

All About Princess Belle

A Magical World...

Belle lives in a magical castle with the Beast and her friends, the Enchanted Objects. She loves to dress up and has lots of pretty gowns. Find out about her style on these pages ...

Add a Touch of Sparkle

Help Belle get ready for a ball by adding some sparkly colours!

Sticker Play

Use your jewel stickers to decorate Belle's dress.

I can count ♡ bows.

Answer on page 91.

Which Outfit?

The Wardrobe helps Belle decide what to wear. Belle's favourite outfit is her floating yellow silk dress.

Accessories

Belle likes her accessories to match her outfit. Her hairband and gloves are the same colour as her dress.

Colourful Clothes

Belle has a lovely, simple style. She wears a different colour each day. Belle always looks stylish, whatever she's wearing!

Inner Beauty

Belle may love pretty dresses, but falling in love with the Beast taught her that true beauty comes from within.

Pretty Jewellery

Can you help Belle get ready for the ball? Give her some beautiful colours.

Sticker Play

Add a sticker when you have finished your colouring.

Put your sticker here.

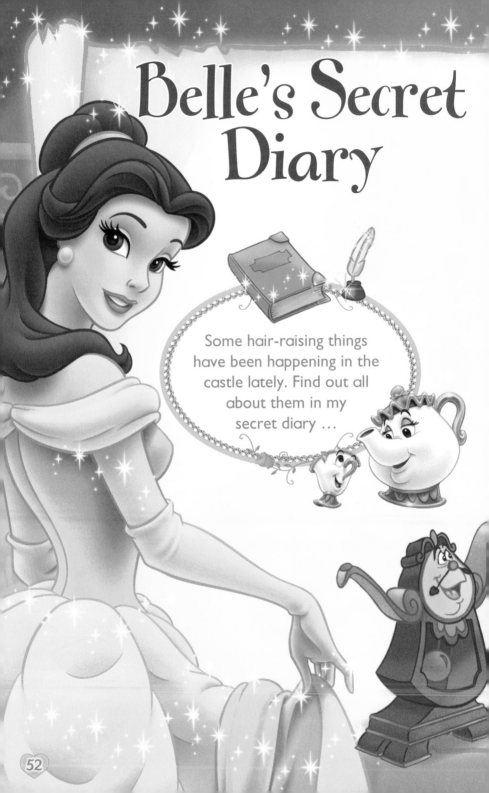

Belle's Secret Diary

Some hair-raising things have been happening in the castle lately. Find out all about them in my secret diary ...

52

Dear Diary ...

Today, I decided to sort out an old wardrobe in the castle. Amongst all the junk, I found a really pretty box. Mrs Potts told me that I shouldn't open it, but I'm really curious. Whatever could be inside?

Dear Diary ...

I couldn't bear wondering any more, so I opened the box! Guess what leapt out ... an enchanted hairbrush and comb! What a surprise! Mrs Potts said there would be trouble.

But a hairbrush and a comb can't cause too much trouble ... can they?

Dear Diary ...

Oh dear, the hairbrush and comb are restyling everything in the castle! They've even tied the fringes on all the curtains into bows!

Dear Diary ...

Oh dear, oh dear, oh dear! The hairbrush and comb decided to restyle the Beast! First, they made his hair stand on end, then they gave him curls, then bunches, then ringlets!

The Beast didn't find it very funny, but it gave me an idea ...

I told the hairbrush and comb
how the Beast likes to have his hair
styled and they made him
look wonderful.

The Beast was very
happy, but now
I need to show
Mrs Potts and the
Enchanted Objects how
useful the hairbrush and
comb can be.

Dear Diary ...

Today, the hairbrush and comb made wonderful wigs for the Enchanted Objects. They all looked lovely, especially Mrs Potts. She says the hairbrush and comb can stay in the castle and don't have to go back in their box.

Dear Diary …

It was my turn to have my hair done by the hairbrush and comb. They gave me the most beautiful hairstyle, with flowers and jewels! I'm so pleased they're going to be around from now on.

The end

Sticker Play

Add a sticker when you have finished reading the story.

Put your sticker here.

Petal Paths

Help Belle find the petal path that will lead
her to the Beast's romantic dinner.

Add some
colour to
the birds.

a.

b.

Start

c.

Which path
leads to the
enchanted
rose?

Finish

Can you count how many birds there are? Write your answer in the heart.

Answers on page 91.

61

Belle's Ball Gowns

Belle loves wearing beautiful ball gowns.
Can you answer the questions about them?

Drop earrings

Matching gloves

Beaded corset

Sparkly clutch bag

Rose trim

1. Which of the details on the right does not appear on the ball gown?

a
b
c

2. Which shoes would match Belle's gown?

a
b
c

How many enchanted roses can you see floating in the air? Write your answer here.

Princess Fun

Use a little bit of magic to help
solve these Princess puzzles.

Lost Belongings

1

One of the princesses has
left some of her things behind
at the ball. Who is it?

Tick the
correct
heart.

a

b

c

In the Forest

2 Which of the forest creatures below isn't in this scene? Tick the correct heart.

a

b

c

Count how many animals are sitting with Snow White.

Look and Colour

Princess Tiana is looking for her frog to kiss. Can you spot him on the page?

3

Colour in Louis.

Sticker Play

Add a sticker when you find the frog.

Put your sticker here.

Lovely Lilies

4

Jasmine is counting the water lilies in the fountain. Answer the questions below.

p a l
l
c
e
a

a How many lilies can you see?

b What word do the letters in the fountain spell?

c Can you find Rajah hiding in the picture?

Answers on page 91.

All About
Princess Aurora

Sleeping Beauty

Aurora was once put
into a deep sleep by evil fairy
Maleficent. She was awoken
by a kiss from her true love.
She's lived happily ever since,
with her family and friends.
Find out more here …

Flora and Aurora are wishing for lovely colours. Make their wish come true.

Sticker Play

Use your stickers to give Aurora some jewellery.

I can count 💜 purple hearts.

Answer on page 91.

Mum and Dad

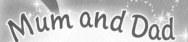

Aurora is the daughter of King Stefan and the Queen. They sent her to the woods for safety. She returned when she was sixteen.

Fairy Fun

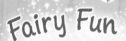

The three good fairies, Flora, Fauna and Merryweather, take care of Aurora. They don't always agree, but they all love her and do their best to make her happy.

Animal Pals

Aurora has lots of animal friends. She sings to them and tells them her secrets. They are always there for her if she needs them.

Handsome Prince

Prince Phillip fell in love
with Aurora before he knew
she was a princess. He
fought his way through
a bush of thorns and battled
a dragon to save her life
with a kiss.

I love ...

Aurora loves her
family and friends. Draw
a picture of someone you
love in the heart.

71

Aurora's Secret Diary

The three good fairies helped me out of a tricky situation, with a little touch of magic! Read all about it in my secret diary ...

Dear Diary ...

I had a bit of a shock this morning.
A letter arrived from King Stefan asking
me to arrange a grand parade. When I
looked at the date, I realised the letter
had been delayed and now I only have
two days to organise everything.

What am I going to do?

Dear Diary ...

Prince Phillip and I have been trying to get everything ready for the parade, but the costumes and decorations are tattered and torn. There's no way we can fix everything in time, so I'm going to visit the three good fairies to see if they have any ideas.

Dear Diary ...

Well, the good fairies were full of ideas as usual, but they couldn't agree on the best plan so nothing has been done and I have even less time now.

I need time to stand still!

Ooooh, that's given me a wonderful idea ...

Dear Diary ...

I asked the fairies if they could stop time! They waved their magic wands to make everything and everyone in the palace freeze ...

... then we quickly set to work, stitching, fixing and polishing, with some help from my animal friends.

Dear Diary ...

The only thing left to do was to make new costumes for everyone. The animals helped me to measure the King, Queen and Prince Phillip ...

... it was quick to do since they were frozen in time and as still as statues!

Dear Diary ...

Today, the good fairies lifted the time spell over the palace. We all put on our new costumes, ready for the grand parade.

The King said everything looked wonderful and the Queen and Prince Phillip agreed!

Dear Diary …

The grand parade was a great success!
Everyone clapped and cheered as the royal
carriage went past.

I think I'll keep the time-freezing spell a secret
between you, me and the good fairies …
you never know when I might need to
use it again!

The end

Sticker Play

Add a sticker
when you have
finished reading
the story.

Put your
sticker here.

Twinkling Tiaras

Can you pass Princess Aurora's tiara test?
Answer the questions on these pages.

a

b

1 Which tiara is the biggest?

2 Which tiaras match? ⬦ and ⬦

c

e

d

f

3 Which tiara is the smallest?

4 Which tiara do these jewels belong to?

Aurora's World

Aurora is enjoying a moment with her friends. There are six differences in the picture on the right. Can you spot them all?

Colour a heart when you spot a difference.

Colour Fun

Colour three birds blue and two birds pink.

Answers on page 91.

Princess Fun

Here are some pretty princess puzzles for you to enjoy!

Dream Match

1 The princesses are daydreaming. Draw a line from each daydream cloud to the correct princess.

a

b

c

Flower Meadow

Snow White is in a flower meadow. Answer the questions below.

2

a
What colour flower is Snow White holding?

b
Do you think it is summer or winter?

c
Point to the rabbit in the picture.

A Flower for Tiana

Follow the tangled ribbon from the start to find which flower Tiana will wear in her hair for the ball.

a

b

c

Start

What is the difference between these two pictures of Ray?

86

Answers on page 91.

Jasmine's Garden

4 Jasmine is in her pretty garden. Add some colour to this lovely picture.

Princess Style

Which princess are you most like?
Answer the questions below to find out.

1 What is your favourite colour?
- a) Green
- b) Yellow
- c) Purple

2 What is your favourite accessory?
- a) Gloves
- b) Hair ribbon
- c) Fan

3 Where is your favourite place to go?
- a) Big city
- b) The woods
- c) A faraway place

4 What is your favourite animal?
- a) Firefly
- b) Rabbit
- c) Tiger

5 What is your favourite hobby?
- a) Cooking
- b) Keeping pets
- c) Dancing

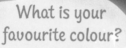

Colour the animals to finish the page.

Mostly a

You are just like Tiana. Strong and feisty, life is fun when you're around.

Mostly b

You are just like Snow White. Gentle and caring, you love animals and nature.

Mostly c

You are just like Jasmine. Adventurous and brave, you make life sparkle.

Princess

Holiday Annual

Answers

Ariel Puzzles

Page 8 – 9
All About Princess Ariel
There are three starfish.

Page 10 – 11
There are four seahorses.

Page 20 – 21
Mer-mysteries
1. a – King Triton's tail is blue.
b – King Triton is holding
a toy dolphin in his hand.
c. The gold trident is behind the
throne.
2. A pearl.

Page 22 – 23
Sea Shadows
1 – d, 2 – f, 3 – e, 4 – b, 5 – c, 6 – a.
The pink and purple shell comes next.

Princess Fun

Page 24 – 25
2. Dwarf c, Doc.

Page 26 – 27
3. b, d, a, c.
4. a – Tiana, b – Jasmine,
c – Snow White.

Cinderella Puzzles

Page 28 – 29
All About Princess Cinderella
There are six birds.

Page 40 – 41
Cinderella's New Dress

Princess Fun

Page 44 – 45
1. Shadow d, the rabbit, isn't in
the pond.
2. You wouldn't usually find a
carrot in a fruit pie.

Page 46-47
3. There are five stars.

4. 1 – c, 2 – a, 3 – b.

Belle Puzzles

Page 48 – 49
All About Princess Belle
There are four bows.

Page 60 – 61
Petal Paths
Path c leads to the Beast.
Path b leads to the enchanted rose.
There are seven birds.

Page 62 – 63
Belle's Ball Gowns
1. c.
2. c.
There are four enchanted roses floating in the air.

Princess Fun

Page 64 – 65
1. c, Jasmine.
2. a, the racoon.
There are seven animals sitting with Snow White.

Page 66 – 67
3. The frog is hiding at the top of the window.
4. a – 7, b – palace, c – Rajah is in the bushes.

Aurora Puzzles

Page 68 – 69
All About Princess Aurora
There are five purple hearts.

Page 80 – 81
Twinkling Tiaras
1. a.
2. c and f.
3. b.
4. e.

Page 82 – 83
Aurora's World

Princess Fun

Page 84 – 85
1. a – Tiana, b – Snow White, c – Jasmine.
2. a – blue, b – summer.

Page 86 – 87
3. c.

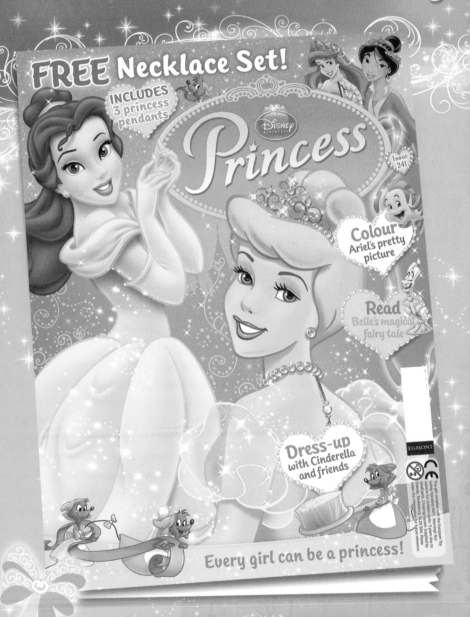